# Daily Literacy Activities

# EARLY AMERICAN HISTORY

**REM 390**

AUTHOR: Sue LaRoy

A TEACHING RESOURCE FROM

R E M E D I A
PUBLICATIONS

EDITOR: **Hannah Bradley**    DESIGNER: **Christina Reville**

**www.rempub.com**

REMEDIA PUBLICATIONS, INC.
SCOTTSDALE, AZ

BLACKLINE MASTERS

RESEARCH-BASED ACTIVITIES
Supports
State &
National
Standards

This product utilizes innovative strategies and proven methods to improve student learning. The product is based upon reliable research and effective practices that have been replicated in classrooms across the United States. Information regarding the Common Core State Standards this product meets is available at www.rempub.com/standards.

# Table of Contents

# Teacher Guide

Literacy means having the ability to read and write. Literacy also means having knowledge or competency in a specified area. The goal of this book is to help students improve reading and writing skills as they learn important information about early American history. If students can successfully read each story in the book, understand the historical facts presented, and then write about what they have learned, they will have become more literate in American history.

The format of this book lends itself to use with students who are functioning below grade level. The information is presented in a way that allows for differentiated instruction. Teacher understanding of a student's ability level will help determine how much material a student can successfully complete in an allotted time on a daily basis. To help keep track of when each part of the lesson is completed, each page has a line for writing the current date.

## BOOK FORMAT

The 14 stories in this book take students on a journey that begins with the early exploration of North America and ends with the formation of a new democratic government. Each three-part story, complete with historical images, is accompanied by five skill-based reading and writing activity pages. These eight pages form a study unit for each story. The stories are numbered to help keep all the story components together.

To encourage students to read and then re-read the text, there is a "locating the information" activity at the bottom of each story page. This simple exercise helps to reinforce key facts from the story. Each story includes words which many students may find challenging. Use of these words is necessary in order to convey historical accuracy. There are three "Words to Know" pages that list difficult or unfamiliar words. Three "People and Places" pages list the names of important people and historic places mentioned in the stories. Two pages of "Enrichment Ideas" offer suggestions for discussion, research, and higher level comprehension questions. The Answer Key provides answers for the comprehension and cloze activity pages.

## READABILITY

A specific challenge for this book was being true to history while simplifying the content. An effort was made to create stories that were rich with important historical information, yet on a level that would be understood by those students reading below grade level.

To accomplish this, short sentences, simple explanations, and plenty of repetition were used whenever possible. A reading specialist reviewed the stories for content and reading ease. Use of the historically relevant vocabulary resulted in an average reading level ranging from 4.0 to 5.5 according to the Flesch-Kincaid Scale. The interest level is grade 5 and up.

## SUGGESTIONS FOR USE

Start by assembling one of the eight-page study units into a folder with the "Words to Know" and "People and Places" lists for that story. Pre-reading strategies can be used based on each student's needs.

### Pre-Reading Strategies

Have the student read the title and study the three images on the story pages. Ask the student what the story might be about. On a sheet of paper, make two columns. One labeled "What I Know" and one labeled "What I Want to Know." Anything the student knows about the topic can be written in one column, and anything the student would like to know can be written in the second column. This may pique interest and give the student a reason to read the story. Point out the "Words to Know" and "People and Places" lists that correspond to the story. Ask the student to identify any unfamiliar words. Talk about the historic figures and groups of people mentioned in the story. Offer help with understanding and the pronunciation of difficult words.

Have students create flashcards for difficult words and allow them to work in pairs to master the words. Some students may benefit from learning the definitions of the words and using them in sentences. Dictionary apps are available for a variety of digital devices that allow students to listen to the definition and pronunciation of a word.

To help set the stage for the story, discuss the countries, regions, colonies, states, and cities referred to in the story. Use either a current or historic map to point out the locations.

## Answer the questions with complete sentences.

1.  What did the Europeans call the native people of North America?

    _____

    _____

2.  Describe what the northeast was like.

    _____

    _____

3.  Name three things that the Woodland People made from wood.

    _____

    _____

4.  What was the most important crop the farmers planted?

    _____

    _____

5.  Which crops were called "the three sisters?"

    _____

    _____

## The Iroquois League                                                          Story 2

The northeastern tribes were often at war with each other. In the early 1600s, five tribes came together to live in peace. The five tribes were the Mohawk, Onondaga, Seneca, Oneida, and Cayuga. These tribes lived mostly in upper New York state and southeastern Canada. They formed the Iroquois League. It was also known as the Iroquois Confederacy.

Each tribe sent representatives to the Great Council. The council members were all men. But the elder women of the tribes chose each member. They also had the power to remove them. The Great Council made important decisions for the good of all the tribes. It was an early example of democracy. They even had a constitution called The Great Law of Peace.

The Iroquois lived in large buildings called longhouses. A longhouse could be up to 25 feet wide by 150 feet long. It had a frame of wooden poles that was covered in elm bark. It had a rounded roof. Up to 12 families could live in each house. Inside there were sleeping platforms along the walls. Shared cooking fires were in the center. There were several longhouses in each village.

1.  Underline the sentence that tells why the five tribes came together.

2.  Underline the sentence that tells what the Great Council did.

3.  Underline the sentence that tells where the Iroquois lived.

Name_____ Date_____

## Answer the questions with complete sentences.

1. Why did the five tribes come together?

   _____

   _____

2. Where did the five tribes live?

   _____

   _____

3. Who chose the members of the Great Council?

   _____

   _____

4. What did the Great Council do?

   _____

   _____

5. Describe what an Iroquois longhouse looked like.

   _____

   _____

## Southeastern Tribes                                              Story 2

The southeastern tribes lived in what is now the southern states of America. This part of the country had fertile soil and a warm climate. The tribes that lived there were excellent farmers. They were skilled artists and builders. They also knew a lot about medicine.

The women planted and harvested the crops. They grew corn, beans, squash, tobacco, sunflowers, and much more. They also gathered nuts, seeds, and fruits. The women made beautiful baskets and pottery. The men hunted with bow and arrow and fished.

## The "Five Civilized Tribes"

The Europeans called the Choctaw, Cherokee, Chickasaw, Creek, and Seminole tribes the "Five Civilized Tribes." They called them this because of the advanced way they lived. And because they were wise about many things. These tribes were also friendly to the European settlers. They helped the settlers and wanted to live in peace.

Southeastern tribes lived in large, well-planned villages. The Florida Seminole lived in homes called chickees. Chickees were built up off the ground. They had wooden frames and thatched roofs. But they had no walls. A cooling breeze could blow through. Other tribes lived in log homes.

The people had a strong connection to the land and nature. They thought everything had a spirit. They held ceremonies to honor the natural world.

1.  Underline the sentence that tells where the southeastern tribes lived.

2.  Underline the sentence that tells what crops were grown.

3.  Underline the two sentences that tell why some tribes were called the "Five Civilized Tribes."

Name_____ Date_____

## Answer the questions with complete sentences.

1.  Where did the southeastern tribes live?

    _____

    _____

2.  Name three things the women of the tribes did.

    _____

    _____

3.  What kind of crops did the southeastern tribes grow?

    _____

    _____

4.  Why were some tribes called the "Five Civilized Tribes?"

    _____

    _____

5.  Describe what a Seminole home called a chickee looked like.

    _____

    _____

**Complete each sentence with a word from the box.**

| | | |
|---|---|---|
| live | planted | advanced |
| great | Woodland | chickees |
| representatives | were | buildings |

1. The _____ People lived in the northeast.

2. The northeast had many lakes, rivers, and _____ forests.

3. Corn was the most important crop the farmers _____.

4. The five tribes came together to _____ in peace.

5. Each tribe sent _____ to the Great Council.

6. The Iroquois lived in large _____ called longhouses.

7. Southeastern tribes _____ skilled artists and builders.

8. The Seminole lived in homes called _____.

9. The "Five Civilized Tribes" had an _____ way of living.

**Read each completed sentence to make sure it makes sense.**

**Write two or more sentences about each topic.**

### Woodland People

_____

_____

_____

_____

### The Iroquois Longhouses

_____

_____

_____

_____

### The Southeastern Tribes

_____

_____

_____

_____

# First Americans: The Plains

The Plains was a vast grassland. It covered 1 million square miles between the Mississippi River and the Rocky Mountains. The Plains stretched from lower Canada in the north to Texas in the south. About 150,000 people from 30 different tribes lived throughout the territory. There were also about 60 million buffalo!

The Plains tribes lived in small groups. They moved a lot. They did not have permanent villages. The people traveled on horses. Most of them lived in tepees. A tepee is cone-shaped. It is made from long poles covered by buffalo hide. It is kind of like a tent. A tepee is easy to move. It can be taken down and put up quickly.

## The Buffalo

There were few trees and little rainfall on the Plains. The native people depended on the buffalo to survive. The tribes followed huge herds of buffalo as they roamed across the plains. Every part of the buffalo was used. The meat was eaten fresh and dried to be eaten later. The skin and

hair was made into clothing, blankets, and teepee covers. Buffalo horns and bones were made into tools, cooking pots, sewing needles, and shields.

1. Underline the sentence that tells how many people lived on the Plains.

2. Underline the sentence that tells how the people traveled.

3. Underline the sentence that tells what the people depended on to survive.

**Answer the questions with complete sentences.**

1.  How many people lived throughout the Plains? How many buffalo?

    _____

    _____


2.  What kind of homes did the Plains tribes live in?

    _____

    _____


3.  How did the Plains tribes travel?

    _____

    _____


4.  What did the Plains tribes depend on for survival?

    _____

    _____


5.  What was buffalo skin and hair used for?

    _____

    _____

Story 3

The Arapaho, Cheyenne, Crow, Osage, and Dakota were some of the Plains tribes. Each tribe spoke a different language. To communicate, they developed a type of sign language. The men of these tribes hunted buffalo on horseback. They were very skilled riders. The men also made weapons. They protected the

tribe by fighting their enemies. The women prepared the food and took care of the children. They dried buffalo skins to make clothing and made beaded necklaces.

The Plains people believed in the Great Spirit. They believed that the land was created by the Great Spirit. It should be shared by all. No one owned the land. The people thought everything on earth was sacred. Every animal had a spirit and should be treated with respect.

**The Dakota (Sioux)**

The Dakota were the largest and most feared of the Plains tribes. They were fierce warriors. The Europeans' name for the Dakota was Sioux. Sioux was a native word for "enemy." To prove their power, the Dakota often fought with other tribes. They also fought against the Europeans.

Children were dearly loved by the Dakota. They were treated with great affection. At an early age, the boys learned to use a bow and arrow. The girls learned to help their mothers. They were well-trained for their adult duties.

1.   Underline the sentence that tells what the tribes did to communicate.

2.   Underline the sentence that tells what the Plains people believed in.

3.   Underline the two sentences that tell who the Dakota were.

**Answer the questions with complete sentences.**

1.  How did the tribes of the Plains communicate with each other?

    _____

    _____

2.  How did the men hunt buffalo?

    _____

    _____

3.  What did the Plains people believe in?

    _____

    _____

4.  Which tribe was the largest and most feared of the Plains tribes?

    _____

    _____

5.  How did the Dakota treat their children?

    _____

    _____

## Tribal War

War was a part of life for the tribes of the Plains. Great warriors were respected and honored. Small bands of warriors raided the villages of their enemies. Before each raid, there was a special ceremony. The warriors took sacred objects with them for protection and strength. The men wanted to win honor and show their courage. They would steal horses and sometimes kill members of another tribe. The tribes suffered many losses because of this.

## The Sun Dance

Music, singing, and dancing was an important part of all ceremonies. The greatest ceremony of all was the Sun Dance. It took place in the summer. People came together during the summer buffalo hunt. The Sun Dance was done to give thanks to the Great Spirit. The dancers also prayed for future help. The celebration lasted four days.

The tribes built a special Sun Dance lodge. A tree was cut down to make a sun dance pole for the center of the lodge. On the fourth day, the men danced around this pole. They looked at the sun as they danced. The dancers asked for good hunting and fighting skills. Some asked for healing powers. The Sun Dance gave people hope for a better future.

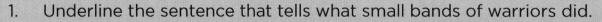

1. Underline the sentence that tells what small bands of warriors did.

2. Underline the sentence that tells why the Sun Dance was done.

3. Underline the sentence that tells what the Sun Dance gave the people.

Name_____ Date_____

## Answer the questions with complete sentences.

1. What did small bands of warriors do?

   _____

   _____

2. Why did warriors take sacred objects with them?

   _____

   _____

3. When did the Sun Dance ceremony take place?

   _____

   _____

4. Why did people do the Sun Dance?

   _____

   _____

5. What did the Sun Dance give people?

   _____

   _____

**Complete each sentence with a word from the box.**

| | | |
|---|---|---|
| sign | life | teepees |
| depended | buffalo | asked |
| greatest | fierce | there |

1. There were about 60 million _____ on the Plains.

2. The Plains people lived in cone-shaped homes called _____.

3. The Plains people _____ on the buffalo to survive.

4. The tribes used _____ language to communicate.

5. The Dakota were _____ warriors.

6. War was a part of _____ for the tribes of the Plains.

7. Before each raid, _____ was a special ceremony.

8. The _____ ceremony of all was the Sun Dance.

9. The dancers _____ for good hunting and fighting skills.

**Read each completed sentence to make sure it makes sense.**

## Answer the questions with complete sentences.

1. Which colony was known as the land of freedom?

   _____

   _____

2. Why did Reverend John Wheelwright and his followers move to New

   Hampshire?

   _____

   _____

3. How much land did King Charles give Lord Baltimore?

   _____

   _____

4. What were Lord Baltimore's goals for his new colony?

   _____

   _____

   _____

5. Who did Lord Baltimore want to come to his colony?

   _____

   _____

## Connecticut

Settlers started moving to Connecticut in the 1630s. Many came from Massachusetts. They wanted to build their own religious communities. Reverend Thomas Hooker was one of those settlers. He and his followers started a settlement known as Hartford. It became the capital of the colony.

Other settlers came to make money. Connecticut had very good land for farming. There was a money-making fur trade. At first, the settlers were at peace with the Native Americans. They traded for furs. But peace did not last long. The settlers took over native land. They brought diseases that killed many native people. The local tribes began to attack the settlers.

## Rhode Island

Rhode Island's first leader was Roger Williams. He was a minister from Massachusetts. Puritan leaders wanted to arrest him. He escaped to Rhode Island. In 1636, he and his followers started the settlement of Providence. The colony became known as a place of religious freedom. It was the first colony to separate religion and government. There was no fighting over religion.

Rhode Island quickly grew and became successful. There were many wealthy farmers and fishermen.

1. Circle the date that settlers started moving to Connecticut.

2. Underline the two sentences that tell why peace with the Native Americans did not last long.

3. Underline the sentence that tells who Rhode Island's first leader was.

**Answer the questions with complete sentences.**

1. Why did settlers start moving to Connecticut?

   _____

   _____

2. What kind of land did Connecticut have?

   _____

   _____

3. Why did peace with the Native Americans not last very long?

   _____

   _____

4. Who was Rhode Island's first leader?

   _____

   _____

5. What did the colony of Rhode Island become known as?

   _____

   _____

**The Carolinas**                                                                                                              Story 6

At first, North and South Carolina were one big colony. It was started in 1663. A group of Englishmen and the governor of Virginian ruled the colony. King Charles II gave them control. But the colony belonged to England.

Settlers came to the Carolinas because they were promised land. Many settlers created very large farms. These farms were called plantations.

African slaves did the hard work on the plantations. Slave ships came to the coast of Carolina. The settlers bought the slaves from slave traders. The slaves showed the plantation owners how to grow rice. Growing rice made the owners very wealthy. The plantation owners  needed the African slaves to grow their crops. But they were very cruel to the slaves. The slaves had no rights. They could not leave the plantation. They had to do whatever the owners told them to do.

The rich plantation owners became very powerful. They wanted to control the government. The colony's leaders wanted to weaken the rich men's power. In 1712, North and South Carolina became separate colonies. Each colony had its own government. The plantation owners did not have as much power.

1.   Underline the sentence that tells who ruled the Carolina colony.

2.   Underline the sentence that tells who did the hard work on the plantations.

3.   Underline the sentence that tells what the slaves showed the plantation owners.

**Answer the questions with complete sentences.**

1.  Who ruled the Carolina colony?

    _____

    _____

2.  Why did settlers come to the Carolinas?

    _____

    _____

3.  Why did plantation owners have slaves?

    _____

    _____

4.  What were the settlers large farms called?

    _____

    _____

5.  How did the plantation owners learn to grow rice?

    _____

    _____

**Complete each sentence with a word from the box.**

| from | freedom | plantation |
| treated | capital | gave |
| diseases | escaped | powerful |

1.  New Hampshire was known as a land of _____.

2.  King Charles _____ Lord Baltimore 12 million acres of land.

3.  Catholics were not _____ well in England.

4.  Hartford became the _____ of Connecticut.

5.  Settlers brought _____ that killed many native people.

6.  Roger Williams _____ to Rhode Island.

7.  Settlers bought slaves _____ slave traders.

8.  Slaves could not leave the _____.

9.  Rich plantation owners became very _____.

**Read each completed sentence to make sure it makes sense.**

**Write two or more sentences about each topic.**

### Lord Baltimore

_____

_____

_____

_____

### Roger Williams

_____

_____

_____

_____

### The Carolinas

_____

_____

_____

_____

Name_____  Date_____

# The Last Colonies: 1664 – 1732

## New York

New York began as a Dutch colony. It was called New Netherland. In 1664, King Charles II said the colony belonged to England. He gave the colony to his brother James, the Duke of York. The King sent warships to make the Dutch leave the territory. They left without a fight. James named his colony New York.

Soon the English colonists made slavery legal in their colony. Slaves were brought in to work on the land. In later years, New York had more slaves than any other northern colony.

The colonists started trading with the Iroquois tribe. They were friendly with the tribe. The Iroquois helped the colonists fight other native tribes. But the colonists did not help the Iroquois fight their enemies. The friendship ended.

## New Jersey

At first, New Jersey was part of the same territory as New York. Then in 1664, the Duke of York gave control of the land to two Englishmen. English and French settlers lived in the new colony. The colony grew. The colonists started their own legislature. The representatives passed laws. One law said only Puritans could vote. The governor didn't like this. He did not let the lawmakers meet again for seven years.

1.  Underline the sentence that tells what the Dutch colony was called.

2.  Underline the sentence that tells what New York had more of than any other northern colony.

3.  Underline the sentence that tells who lived in the New Jersey colony.

## Answer the questions with complete sentences.

1. What was the Dutch colony called?

   _____

   _____

2. What did the English colonists make legal in their colony?

   _____

   _____

3. Who did the colonists start trading with?

   _____

   _____

4. Why did the colonists' friendship with the Iroquois end?

   _____

   _____

5. Who lived in the New Jersey colony?

   _____

   _____

## Pennsylvania

William Penn was a wealthy Quaker. In England the Quakers were not treated well. The Quakers wanted their own colony in the New World. King Charles II owed William's father money. To pay him back, he gave William land in America. In 1680, the colony of Pennsylvania was created.

As a Quaker, William Penn believed in kindness, honesty, and fairness. People from other religions could live in his colony. He also welcomed people from other countries. William made treaties with the local Delaware tribe. He treated them with respect. He did not steal their land. Colonists and native people both had the same rights. This allowed them to live in peace.

A council of 72 men made the rules for the colony. The council created the Great Law. The Great Law made people of all religions equal. They could all vote. By the mid-1700s, more than 180,000 people lived in Pennsylvania.

## Delaware

William Penn was given Delaware as part of his colony. The people in Delaware did not get along with the Quakers. The Delaware colonists wanted an Army. The Quakers did not believe in fighting. In 1701, William made Delaware and Pennsylvania into two separate colonies. Delaware was the smallest of all the colonies.

1. Underline the sentence that tells who William Penn was.

2. Underline the sentence that tells what William Penn believed in.

3. Underline the two sentences that tell why the people of Delaware did not get along with the Quakers.

**Answer the questions with complete sentences.**

1. Who was William Penn?

   _____

   _____

2. Why did the King give William Penn land in America?

   _____

   _____

3. What did William Penn believe in?

   _____

   _____

4. What was the Great Law?

   _____

   _____

5. Why did the people of Delaware not get along with the Quakers?

   _____

   _____

## Georgia

The last colony to be created was Georgia. A group called the Georgia Trustees wanted a colony where they could send poor English people. It would give the people a chance for a better life. King George II thought it was a good idea. It was the only colony that got money from the English government. Georgia was started in 1732.

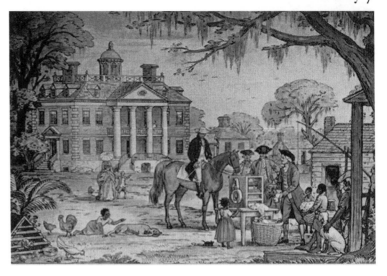

At first, Georgia did not allow slavery. The Trustees did not want plantations in Georgia. Instead they wanted the colonists to guard the border with Florida. Florida was ruled by the Spanish. The colonists were supposed to stop any attacks from Spanish soldiers. Later, slavery became legal. Many slaves ended up working for rich Georgia plantation owners.

## The Thirteen Colonies

The thirteen colonies were Virginia, Massachusetts, New Hampshire, Maryland, Connecticut, Rhode Island, North Carolina, South Carolina, New York, New Jersey, Pennsylvania, Delaware, and Georgia. These thirteen colonies were the beginning of the United States of America.

English settlers created each colony. The colonies started in different ways. They all had different purposes. Some people wanted religious freedom. Some people just wanted to make money. But everyone wanted a fresh start in the New World.

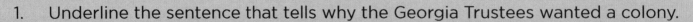

1. Underline the sentence that tells why the Georgia Trustees wanted a colony.

2. Underline the sentence that tells what the colonists were supposed to do.

3. Underline the sentence that tells what the thirteen colonies were the beginning of.

Name_____ Date_____

## Answer the questions with complete sentences.

1. Why did the Georgia Trustees want a colony?

   _____

   _____

2. What did Georgia get from the English government that no other colony got?

   _____

   _____

3. Why didn't the Trustees want plantations in Georgia?

   _____

   _____

4. What happened after slavery became legal in Georgia?

   _____

   _____

5. What was the beginning of the United States of America?

   _____

   _____

## Complete each sentence with a word from the box.

| | | |
|---|---|---|
| wealthy | poor | religions |
| fighting | thirteen | friendly |
| named | settlers | slaves |

1. The Duke of York _____ his colony New York.

2. At first, the colonists were _____ with the Iroquois.

3. English and French _____ lived in New Jersey.

4. William Penn was a _____ Quaker.

5. People from all _____ could live in Pennsylvania.

6. The Quakers did not believe in _____.

7. Georgia would give _____ people a chance for a better life.

8. Many _____ worked for rich Georgia plantation owners.

9. The _____ colonies were the beginning of the United States of America.

**Read each completed sentence to make sure it makes sense.**

**Answer the questions with complete sentences.**

1.  Why did the colonists come to the colonies?

    _____

    _____

2.  What were the king and the British government determined to do?

    What were the colonists determined to do?

    _____

    _____

3.  What kind of army and navy did the British have?

    _____

    _____

4.  Why were the colonists worried they would not be able to stand up to

    the British?

    _____

    _____

5.  Why did the colonists have to unite?

    _____

    _____

## The Militia

It seemed like a fight with the British was coming. Many British soldiers were already in the colonies. The colonists decided to form a militia to defend themselves. The militia was a volunteer group of regular citizens. It included men of all ages from grandfathers to teenage boys. There were farmers, trappers, doctors,  lawyers, and businessmen. The militia were not trained soldiers. They did not have uniforms. They had to use their own weapons. They came together to fight for what they believed in. The men started training in the fields after work.

## Minutemen

Minutemen were small groups of specially trained men. They were usually the youngest and strongest of the militia. They were trained to be ready to fight at a moments notice. They would be the first into battle.

## First Continental Congress

The First Continental Congress was a meeting of delegates from 12 of the 13 colonies. Georgia did not send anyone. They met on September 5, 1774 in Philadelphia. The meeting happened because of the Intolerable Acts passed by Britain. There was lots of arguing about what should be done. The delegates were not used to working together. The meeting lasted about a month. Finally, the delegates agreed to send a letter to King George. The letter said they would remain loyal to Britain. But the king had to respect their rights. The king ignored the letter.

1. Underline the sentence that tells how the colonists decided to defend themselves.

2. Circle the date the First Continental Congress met.

3. Underline the sentence that tells what the delegates finally agreed to do.

**Answer the questions with complete sentences.**

1. What kind of men volunteered for the militia?

   _____

   _____

2. Why did the men of the militia come together?

   _____

   _____

3. Who were the Minutemen?

   _____

   _____

4. When and where did the First Continental Congress meet?

   _____

   _____

5. What did the delegates finally agree to do?

   _____

   _____

## The Second Continental Congress

Things continued to get worse in the colonies. There was fighting between the colonists and the British soldiers. People were dying. A war with Britain had begun. The Second Continental Congress met in Philadelphia on May 10, 1775. The delegates had to decide what to do about the war that was starting.

Sam Adams and John Hancock wanted the colonies to declare their independence from Britain. They were delegates from Massachusetts. They didn't think Britain was ever going to treat the colonies fairly. Delegates from some of the other colonies disagreed. People in the colonies made a lot of money selling lumber, tobacco and other goods to the British. They didn't want to lose that income. Plus, some colonists still felt like they were British. They weren't ready to turn away from the king. The delegates argued for months. In the meantime, the war was still going on.

## The Continental Army

The delegates could all agree they wanted to win the war. The militia was fighting hard. But they were no match for the British soldiers. Something else needed to be done. The delegates created the Continental Army. They asked George Washington to be the Commander-in-Chief. The men in this army would be paid. They would have uniforms and would be given weapons. They would get special training. The Continental Army and the militia would work together to try to defeat the British.

1.  Underline the sentence that tells when the Second Continental Congress met.
2.  Underline the sentence that tells who wanted the colonies to declare their independence from Britain.
3.  Circle the name of the person who was to be the Commander-in-Chief of the Continental Army.

**Answer the questions with complete sentences.**

1. When did the Second Continental Congress take place?

   _____

   _____

2. Who were Sam Adams and John Hancock?

   _____

   _____

3. Why did some delegates disagree about declaring independence
   from Britain?

   _____

   _____

4. What could all of the delegates agree on?

   _____

   _____

5. Who was the Commander-in-Chief of the Continental Army?

   _____

   _____

**Complete each sentence with a word from the box.**

| defend | free | ignored |
|--------|------|---------|
| lasted | king | largest |
| between | militia | delegates |

1. The colonists had come to the colonies to be

   _____.

2. Britain had the world's _____ navy.

3. The colonists had no army to _____ them.

4. The _____ was a volunteer group of regular
   citizens.

5. The meeting of the First Continental Congress
   _____ about a month.

6. The king _____ the letter from the delegates.

7. A war _____ the colonists and the British had
   begun.

8. Some colonists weren't ready to turn away from the

   _____.

9. The _____ created the Continental Army.

**Read each completed sentence to make sure it makes sense.**

## Write two or more sentences about each topic.

### The Militia

_____

_____

_____

_____

### The First Continental Congress

_____

_____

_____

_____

### The Continental Army

_____

_____

_____

_____

# The Declaration of Independence

The colonists had worked very hard to make a new life in America. Many felt they were now Americans. They had left their British life behind. They wanted their freedom now! But for some, it was not that easy. These colonists still felt like they were British. They were loyal to the king. They still had family in Britain. They wanted a chance to work things out.

On July 8, 1775, some of the delegates to the Second Continental Congress wrote the king a second letter. The letter listed ways to solve their problems with the king. They asked that the colonies be treated more fairly. The king refused to read the letter. He was angry with the colonists.

## A Big Decision

The delegates of the Second Continental Congress had been meeting for over a year. They did not want to make a mistake. The future of all the colonists depended on what they decided. While the Congress was meeting, several battles had taken place. Many British and American soldiers had been killed.

Finally all the delegates made a decision. It was time to declare their independence from Britain. In May of 1776, the Congress chose five men to write a declaration. It would be an official statement. It would say the colonies were breaking away from Britain.

1.  Underline the sentence that tells what happened on July 8, 1775.
2.  Underline the sentence that tells why the king refused to read the letter.
3.  Underline the sentence that tells what the delegates finally agreed about.

**Answer the questions with complete sentences.**

1. When did some of the delegates write a second letter to the king?

   _____

   _____

2. What did the delegates ask the king in the second letter?

   _____

   _____

3. What happened when the king got the second letter?

   _____

   _____

4. Why was it important for the delegates to make the right decision?

   _____

   _____

5. What did all the delegates finally decide?

   _____

   _____

## Who wrote the Declaration of Independence?                    Story II

The five men who were supposed to write the document were John Adams, Roger Sherman, Benjamin Franklin, Robert Livingston, and Thomas Jefferson. The men talked about what the document should say. But they agreed it would be easier for just one man to write it. They chose Thomas Jefferson.

THE DECLARATION COMMITTEE.

Jefferson was a young lawyer from Virginia. He was known as a very good writer. He had written other important papers. Jefferson took the job very seriously. His writing had to speak for all of the colonists. It had to clearly say what they wanted. He worked on the document for 17 days. Next he showed the document to John Adams and Benjamin Franklin. They made a few changes. The three men gave the Declaration of Independence to the Congress to vote on.

## What did the Declaration of Independence say?

The first part of the document said that all men were created equal. Everyone should have certain basic rights. Some of these rights were "life, liberty, and the pursuit of happiness." In the second part of the document, the delegates listed what they thought Britain had done wrong. It told why the colonists wanted their freedom. The last part of the document said that the colonies were now free and independent states. They could have their own government.

1.   Underline the sentence that tells who was chosen to write the document.

2.   Underline the sentence that tells how long Jefferson worked on the document.

3.   Underline the sentence that tells what some of the rights were in the document.

**Answer the questions with complete sentences.**

1. Who was chosen to write the Declaration of Independence?

   _____

   _____

2. Who made a few changes to the document after it was written?

   _____

   _____

3. What is one thing the first part of the Declaration of Independence said?

   _____

   _____

4. What is one thing the second part of the Declaration of Independence said?

   _____

   _____

5. What is one thing the last part of the Declaration of Independence said?

   _____

   _____

## Signing the Declaration of Independence

It was uncommon for people to declare the right to rule themselves. It was more common for people to be ruled by royalty and the wealthy and powerful. This was a big step for the colonists to take. All the delegates gathered to vote on the declaration.

On July 4, 1776 the delegates voted yes! They wanted independence from Britain. Fifty-six men signed the declaration. They represented all of the colonies. Signing the document was dangerous. Any signers caught by the British would be hanged as traitors.

## A Big Celebration

Copies of the Declaration of Independence were sent to all the colonies. When people saw it they cheered! There were parties, bands played, and bells rang. The colonists were excited about creating their own government. On July 4, 1777, the first Independence Day celebration was held in Philadelphia.

There were fireworks and a big parade. But this was just the beginning. The king did not accept the declaration. He refused to let go of the colonies. The colonists still had to win the war with Britain.

1.  Underline the sentence that tells who most commonly ruled the people.

2.  Underline the sentence that tells what would happen if any of the signers were caught by the British.

3.  Underline the sentence that tells what happened at the first Independence Day celebration.

Name_____ Date_____

## Answer the questions with complete sentences.

1. Why was it uncommon for people to declare the right to rule themselves?

   _____

   _____

2. Why did the delegates vote yes! on July 4, 1776?

   _____

   _____

3. Why was signing the declaration dangerous?

   _____

   _____

4. What happened when people saw copies of the Declaration of Independence?

   _____

   _____

5. What happened at the first Independence Day celebration?

   _____

   _____

**Complete each sentence with a word from the box.**

| document | write | voted |
|----------|-------|-------|
| days | solve | win |
| loyal | equal | five |

1.  Some colonists were still _____ to the king.

2.  The second letter listed ways to _____ the problems with the king.

3.  In May of 1776, the Congress chose _____ men to write a declaration.

4.  Thomas Jefferson was chosen to _____ the document.

5.  Jefferson worked on the document for 17 _____.

6.  The declaration said that all men were created _____.

7.  On July 4, 1776, the delegates _____ yes!

8.  Signing the _____ was dangerous.

9.  The colonists still had to _____ the war with Britain.

**Read each completed sentence to make sure it makes sense.**

**Write two or more sentences about each topic.**

### The Declaration of Independence

_____

_____

_____

_____

### Thomas Jefferson

_____

_____

_____

_____

### July 4, 1776

_____

_____

_____

# The Revolutionary War (1775-1783)

Story 12

## The Beginning of the War

Colonists who joined the militia were called Patriots. They wanted freedom from Britain. The Patriots were secretly storing guns and gunpowder in Concord, Massachusetts. They wanted to be ready if the British attacked. British General Thomas Gage got orders to take the guns and gunpowder from Concord.

Under the cover of darkness, Gage and 700 British soldiers marched to Concord. They wanted to surprise the Patriots. But some of the Patriots found out about the plan. That night, Paul Revere and William Dawes jumped on their horses. They rode off to warn the Patriot leaders that the British were coming!

The British soldiers got as far as Lexington. They were stopped by Captain John Parker and 77 minutemen. It was the early morning of April 19, 1775. A shot was fired. No one knows which side fired the first shot. It was called the "shot heard 'round the world" because it started the Revolutionary War.

More shots were fired. The Patriots were outnumbered. Eight Patriots died and 10 were wounded. The British left and went on to Concord. More of the Patriot militia was in Concord. The guns and gunpowder were safe. The militia fought bravely until the British retreated. By the end of the day, 273 British and 95 Americans lost their lives.

1. Underline the sentence that tells what the Patriots were secretly doing.
2. Underline the sentences that tells what Paul Revere and William Dawes did after they jumped on their horses.
3. Circle the date the first shot of the Revolutionary War was fired.

**Answer the questions with complete sentences.**

1. Why were the Patriots secretly storing guns and gunpowder?

   _____

   _____

2. Who warned the Patriot leaders that the British were coming?

   _____

   _____

3. When was the first shot of the Revolutionary War fired?

   _____

   _____

4. Who fired the first shot?

   _____

   _____

5. Why was the first shot called "the shot heard 'round the world?"

   _____

   _____

Story 12

## The War Continues

Throughout 1776 and 1777 there were many battles. The British army was bigger and stronger. They often won the battles. The king kept sending more soldiers to defeat the Patriots. Not all of the colonists were Patriots. Some were still loyal to the king. They were called Loyalists. The king wanted the Loyalists to fight against the Patriots.

In August of 1776, the British took over New York City. Loyalists gathered there to help the British. It was a bad time for the Patriots. The men were discouraged. Some Patriots left the Continental Army. They felt it was useless to fight. They would never be able to win the war.

## An Important Victory

Things changed on an icy cold Christmas night in 1776. George Washington and his men crossed the Delaware River. They surprised British troops who were celebrating the holiday. The Patriots easily won two battles. The first battle they won was at Trenton, New Jersey. Then a few days later, they won at Princeton, New Jersey. Winning these battles was an important victory. It gave the Patriots hope. There was a new determination to beat the British!

1.  Underline the sentence that tells what the colonists still loyal to the king were called.
2.  Underline the two sentences that tell why some Patriots left the Continental Army.
3.  Underline the two sentences that tell why winning the two battles was an important victory.

Name_____ Date_____

## Answer the questions with complete sentences.

1. Why were some of the colonists called Loyalists?

   _____

   _____

2. Where did the Loyalists gather to help the British?

   _____

   _____

3. Why did some Patriots leave the Continental Army?

   _____

   _____

4. Who crossed the Delaware with his men on Christmas night?

   _____

   _____

5. How did the Patriots feel after they won the battles at Trenton and

   Princeton?

   _____

   _____

## Help from the French and the Spanish

Benjamin Franklin went to France to ask for help with the war. Britain was an enemy of France. It was a chance for the French to get back at the British. In 1778, France joined the Revolutionary War on the side of the Americans. France gave America money and sent over 10,000 soldiers. The French soldiers fought alongside the American Patriots. It was the beginning of a long friendship between France and America.

In 1779, the Spanish joined the fight. Britain was an old enemy of Spain too. Spain also wanted to get back at the British. Spanish soldiers attacked British troops in the south.

## The End of the War

Now the British were fighting the French and Spanish as well as the Americans. This was hard on the British soldiers. They began losing more and

more battles. The French helped the Americans win the last major battle of the war. It was the Battle of Yorktown. On October 19, 1781, General Cornwallis surrendered all his troops to George Washington. The British knew they had lost the colonies.

Now Britain and America had to agree on a peace treaty. Representatives from America and Britain met in France. Britain agreed to accept the United States of America as an independent nation. On September 3, 1783, the Treaty of Paris was signed. This was the end of the Revolutionary War.

1. Underline the sentences that tell when France joined the Revolutionary War.

2. Circle the name of the last major battle of the war.

3. Underline the sentence that tells what happened on September 3, 1783.

**Answer the questions with complete sentences.**

1.  When did France join the Revolutionary War?

    _____

    _____

2.  Who attacked British troops in the south?

    _____

    _____

3.  What is the name of the last major battle of the war?

    _____

    _____

4.  Who surrendered his troops to George Washington?

    _____

    _____

5.  What treaty was signed at the end of the Revolutionary War?

    _____

    _____

**Complete each sentence with a word from the box.**

| stopped | secretly | important |
|---------|----------|-----------|
| against | alongside | helped |
| ended | useless | soldiers |

1. The Patriots were _____ storing guns and gunpowder.

2. General Gage and 700 British _____ marched to Concord.

3. The British were _____ by Captain John Parker and 77 minutemen.

4. The king wanted the Loyalists to fight _____ the Patriots.

5. Some Patriots thought is was _____ to fight the British.

6. General George Washington won an _____ victory.

7. The French soldiers fought _____ the American Patriots.

8. The French _____ the Americans win the Battle of Yorktown.

9. The Revolutionary War _____ September 3, 1783.

**Read each completed sentence to make sure it makes sense.**

**Write two or more sentences about each topic.**

### Patriots

_____

_____

_____

_____

### Loyalists

_____

_____

_____

_____

### Battle of Yorktown

_____

_____

_____

_____

# The Constitution of the United States

Story 13

The Constitution is America's most important document. It was signed on September 7, 1787. The Constitution creates the federal government. It is the supreme law of the United States. The Constitution guarantees certain basic rights for all U.S. citizens.

The Constitution has three main purposes:

**1. Separation of Powers**

It divides the federal government into three branches: legislative, executive, and judicial. There are checks and balances. No one branch has too much power. The three branches must work together to run the country.

**2. Division of Federal and State Power**

It divides power between the federal government and the states. The federal government has a set of laws that give it certain powers over the states. But each state also has its own laws. If there is a conflict between state law and federal law, the federal law usually wins.

**3. Protection of Personal Liberty**

It protects the personal freedom of all U. S. citizens from interference by the federal government. In 1791, the Bill of Rights became part of the Constitution. This bill added many more citizen rights, including freedom of speech, freedom of religion, and freedom of the press.

1. Underline the sentence that tells what the Constitution creates.
2. Underline the sentence that tells what the Constitution guarantees.
3. Underline the sentence that names the three branches of government.

Name_____ Date_____

## Answer the questions with complete sentences.

1. In what year was the Constitution of the United States signed?

   _____

   _____

2. What does the Constitution create?

   _____

   _____

3. What does the Constitution guarantee?

   _____

   _____

4. What are the three branches of the federal government?

   _____

   _____

5. What must the three branches of the federal government do?

   _____

   _____

## Why did America need the Constitution?

The war with Great Britain had started. The members of the Continental Congress decided they needed to set up a national government. The 13 new states wanted to defeat the British. They worked on a document to unite the states.

In 1781, the Articles of Confederation was completed. It was the first constitution. In the first constitution, the national government was weak. It did not have much power. Each state acted like it was its own country.

America finally won its freedom from Great Britain in 1783. It was now its own nation! Many leaders thought a strong national government was needed. It should have more power. With a strong government, the new nation could grow and remain safe. A new constitution was needed.

In 1786, Alexander Hamilton asked for a meeting to talk about a new constitution. Hamilton was a lawyer and politician from New York. He wanted a constitutional convention. All 13 states would send delegates to a meeting in Philadelphia.

1. Underline the sentence that tells what the Continental Congress decided.

2. Underline the sentence that tells when America won its freedom from Great Britain.

3. Underline the sentence that tells who Alexander Hamilton was.

**Answer the questions with complete sentences.**

1. What did members of the Continental Congress decide when they met?

   _____

   _____

2. What did the members of the Continental Congress work on?

   _____

   _____

3. When was the Articles of Confederation completed?

   _____

   _____

4. In the first constitution, what was the national government like?

   _____

   _____

5. How could a strong government help America?

   _____

   _____

## Who wrote the Constitution?

On May 25, 1787, the Constitutional Convention began. It was held at Independence Hall in Philadelphia. There were 55 delegates. All the states sent representatives except Rhode Island. The delegates were all well-educated men. They were bankers, merchants, farmers, and lawyers. These men came together to form a new kind of government.

George Washington became president of the convention. James Madison wrote the document that was the model for the Constitution. He was known as the "Father of the Constitution."

There was debate among the delegates. They discussed what should be in the Constitution. Finally, in September of 1787, a five-member committee wrote the final document. The five men included Alexander Hamilton and James Madison.

### The Constitution Today

It has been more than 200 years since the Constitution was created. America now has 50 states that stretch across the entire continent and beyond. More than 327 million people now live in the U.S. The country has gone through many changes. But the Constitution has survived and is still the supreme law of the United States.

1.  Circle the name of the place where the Constitutional Convention was held.
2.  Underline the sentence that tells why the delegates came together.
3.  Underline the sentence that tells what the delegates discussed.

Name_____ Date_____

## Answer the questions with complete sentences.

1. When did the Constitutional Convention begin?

   _____

   _____

2. Which of the 13 states did not send a representative to the

   Convention?

   _____

   _____

3. Why did the delegates to the Constitutional Convention get

   together?

   _____

   _____

4. Who became president of the Constitutional Convention?

   _____

   _____

5. Who became known as the "Father of the Constitution"?

   _____

   _____

**Complete each sentence with a word from the box.**

| | | |
|---|---|---|
| executive | sent | divided |
| federal | written | should |
| important | was | citizens |

1.  The Constitution of the United States is an

    _____ document.

2.  The Constitution _____ signed in 1787.

3.  The Constitution creates the _____ government.

4.  The federal government is _____ into three

    branches.

5.  One of the branches is called the _____ branch.

6.  Twelve states _____ delegates to a meeting.

7.  The delegates discussed what _____ be in the

    Constitution.

8.  The Constitution protects the rights of all U.S.

    _____.

9.  The Constitution was _____ more than 200

    years ago.

**Read each completed sentence to make sure it makes sense.**

**Write two or more sentences about each topic.**

### Articles of Confederation

_____

_____

_____

_____

### Alexander Hamilton

_____

_____

_____

_____

### James Madison

_____

_____

_____

_____

# A New Government

The leaders of the newly created United States of America had to decide how to set up the government. They were doing something new. There were no governments in Europe at the time where people chose their own leaders and ruled themselves. This type of government is called a democracy. A lot of decisions had to be made about how things would work.

## The Electoral College

The delegates at the Constitutional Convention made many of these decisions. One of the most important decisions was about voting. They all agreed there should be a president. The president would lead the country. He would be voted into office by the people.

There was disagreement about how that vote would happen. Some delegates wanted every citizen to vote. The most popular candidate would be elected president. Others felt that would not be fair. They thought people would only vote for a candidate from their own state. That meant the larger states had more power. They would get to pick who was president.

It was decided that the Electoral College would be the fairest way to vote. Men called electors would be chosen from each state. Those men would vote for the president on behalf of their state.

1.  Underline the sentence that tells what the new type of government is called.

2.  Underline the sentence that tells what one of the most important decisions was about.

3.  Underline the sentence that tells what would be the fairest way to vote.

Name_____ Date_____

## Answer the questions with complete sentences.

1. What type of government were the leaders of the United States setting up?

   _____

   _____

2. What was one of the most important decisions the delegates of the Constitutional Convention had to make?

   _____

   _____

3. How would the president get into office?

   _____

   _____

4. Why did some delegates not want every citizen to vote?

   _____

   _____

5. What did the delegates decide would be the fairest way to vote?

   _____

   _____

## Electing the First President and Vice President

Story 14

The first presidential election was in 1789. Each state had to choose their electors to the Electoral College. The number of electors depended on the number of senators and representatives from each state. Either the voters or the state legislature chose these men.

Only white men who were property owners could vote. The signers of the constitution had strong beliefs. They believed only people who paid property taxes should have a say in the government. They also thought only white men were smart enough to vote. This meant less than 2% of Americans could vote in the first election.

George Washington was running for president. Many people knew about him. He was a hero of the Revolutionary War. He was very popular. People respected and trusted him. All the electors agreed he was the best person to run the country. George Washington was elected the first president of the United States of America.

John Adams was elected as vice president. Until 1804, the vice president was elected separately. He was the candidate with the second most votes. After 1804, the president and the vice president were elected together.

1. Underline the sentence that tells when the first presidential election was held.

2. Underline the sentence that tells who could vote.

3. Underline the sentence that tells how people felt about George Washington.

Name_____ Date_____

## Answer the questions with complete sentences.

1.  When was the first presidential election?

    _____

    _____

2.  Why did the signers of the constitution believe only white men who were property owners should vote?

    _____

    _____

3.  What percentage of Americans could vote in the first election?

    _____

    _____

4.  Who was elected the first president of the United States of America?

    _____

    _____

5.  Who was elected vice president?

    _____

    _____

**The First Cabinet**                                                   Story 14

The president is the leader of the government. But he does not work alone. He picks people to give him advice and help. This group of people are his cabinet. He can talk to them about important decisions. Thomas Jefferson, Alexander Hamilton, and Henry Knox were all a part of George Washington's cabinet.

**The First Congress**

The first Congress was also elected in 1789. Congress includes the Senate and the House of Representatives. There were 26 senators. To be fair, there are two senators from each state. It doesn't matter how many people live in the state. There were 56 representatives. The number of

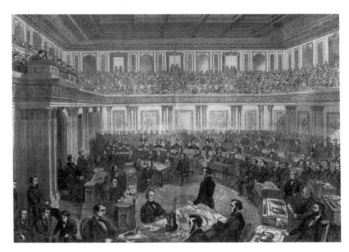

representatives from each state is based on its population. Congress votes on laws that affect the daily lives of all Americans. Congress can pass a law. But the president has to decide whether or not to sign the law.

**The First Supreme Court**

There were no federal courts before 1789. Congress passed a law to start a federal court system. Federal courts make sure federal laws are followed. The nation's most powerful court is the US Supreme Court. The first Supreme Court had six judges. The president chose each judge. Today, there are nine judges on the Supreme Court. The judges hear cases and make a decision. Their decisions are final.

1.   Underline the sentence that tells who the group of people that help the president are.

2.   Underline the sentence that tells what Congress votes on.

3.   Underline the sentence that tells what federal courts do.

**Answer the questions with complete sentences.**

1. Who were some of the people in George Washington's cabinet?

   _____

   _____

2. How many senators were in the first Congress? How many

   representatives?

   _____

   _____

3. What does Congress vote on?

   _____

   _____

4. What do federal courts do?

   _____

   _____

5. How many judges were on the first Supreme Court?

   _____

   _____

**Complete each sentence with a word from the box.**

| | | |
|---|---|---|
| behalf | office | leader |
| separately | six | includes |
| democracy | trusted | senators |

1. The new government was called a _____.

2. The president would be voted into _____ by the people.

3. Electors would vote for the president on _____ of their state.

4. People _____ and respected George Washington.

5. Until 1804, the vice president was elected

   _____.

6. The president is the _____ of the government.

7. Congress _____ the Senate and House of Representatives.

8. There were 26 _____ in the first Congress.

9. The first Supreme Court had _____ judges.

**Read each completed sentence to make sure it makes sense.**

**Write two or more sentences about each topic.**

### The Electoral College

_____

_____

_____

_____

### George Washington

_____

_____

_____

_____

### The Supreme Court

_____

_____

_____

_____

# WORDS TO KNOW

## Story 1 Early Explorers

| | | | |
|---|---|---|---|
| attack | explorers | religion | voyage |
| conquistadors | mission | route | |
| dangerous | precious | settlements | |

## Story 2   First Americans: The East

| | | | |
|---|---|---|---|
| civilized | council | medicine | southeastern |
| Confederacy | knowledge | northeastern | surrounded |
| continent | League | platform | tobacco |

## Story 3   First Americans: The Plains

| | | | |
|---|---|---|---|
| celebration | depended | lodge | suffered |
| ceremony | enemies | permanent | warriors |
| communicate | fierce | sacred | |

## Story 4   First Americans: The West

| | | | |
|---|---|---|---|
| apartments | outstanding | spectacular | wealth |
| commoners | resources | throughout | |
| communities | social | watertight | |

## Story 5   The First Colonies

| | | | |
|---|---|---|---|
| Christianity | example | settlers | survive |
| colony | religious | strict | |

## Story 6    The Next Colonies

| | | | |
|---|---|---|---|
| agree | diseases | plantations | valuable |
| Catholics | minister | Protestants | |

## Story 7    The Last Colonies

| | | |
|---|---|---|
| territory | representatives | treaties |
| legislature | Quaker | |

## Story 8    Servants and Slaves in the Colonies

| | | | |
|---|---|---|---|
| auctions | crammed | indentured | livestock |
| blacksmith | harvested | kidnapped | |

## Story 9    Trouble in the Colonies

| | | | |
|---|---|---|---|
| colonists | protesters | representation | tax |
| Intolerable | punish | riots | taxation |
| protests | refused | ruined | |

## Story 10    The Colonies Unite

| | | | |
|---|---|---|---|
| Continental Congress | delegates | ignored | volunteer |
| | determined | militia | |
| declare | | | |
| | disagreed | resist | |
| defeat | | | |

## Story 11    The Declaration of Independence

decision

declaration

document

equal

independence

liberty

pursuit

Second Continental Congress

traitors

## Story 12    The Revolutionary War

determination

discouraged

loyal

Revolutionary

retreated

surrendered

## Story 13    The Constitution of the United States

Articles of Confederation

conflict

constitution

constitutional convention

debate

executive

federal

guarantees

judicial

interference

legislative

model

supreme

## Story 14    A New Government

behalf

democracy

disagreement

electors

Electoral College

senators

cabinet

Congress

## Story 1 Early Explorers

**PEOPLE**

Columbus
European
Italian
Juan Ponce de Leon

Jacques Cartier
Frances Drake
Queen Elizabeth I

**PLACES**

Asia
China
Caribbean
England

France
Spain
Montreal
St. Lawrence River

## Story 2 First Americans: The East

**PEOPLE**

Onondaga
Mohawk
Iroquois
Choctaw
Chickasaw
Cherokee
Cayuga

Creek
Seminole
Seneca
Oneida
Woodland People

**PLACES**

Mississippi River
North Carolina
Ohio Valley
Great Lakes
New York
Canada
Florida

## Story 3 First Americans: The Plains

**PEOPLE**

Cheyenne
Osage
Sioux (Dakota)

Crow
Arapaho

**PLACES**

Rocky Mountains
Texas

## Story 4 First Americans: The West

**PEOPLE**

Apache
Navajo
Pueblo
Hopi
Zuni
Pomo

**PLACES**

Northwest
New Mexico
Arizona
Nevada
California
Pacific Ocean

Coast Mountain Range
Oregon
Washington
British Columbia

## Story 5    The First Colonies

**PEOPLE**

Pilgrims

Puritans

King James

John Rolfe

Wampanoag

**PLACES**

Jamestown

Plymouth Rock/Plymouth

Massachusetts

Virginia

## Story 6    The Next Colonies

**PEOPLE**

King Charles

Lord Baltimore

Reverend John Wheelwright

Reverend Thomas Hooker

Roger Williams

**PLACES**

New Hampshire

Maryland

Connecticut

Hartford

Rhode Island

The Carolinas

## Story 7    The Last Colonies

**PEOPLE**

Duke of York

Dutch

William Penn

**PLACES**

New York

New Jersey

Pennsylvania

Delaware

Georgia

## Story 8    Servants and Slaves in the Colonies

**PEOPLE**

Africans

**PLACES**

Atlantic Ocean

## Story 9    Trouble in the Colonies

**PLACES**

Great Britain

Boston

## Story 10   The Colonies Unite

**PEOPLE**

King George

Sam Adams

John Hancock

George Washington

**PLACES**

Philadelphia

## Story 11   The Declaration of Independence

**PEOPLE**

John Adams

Roger Sherman

Benjamin Franklin

Robert Livingston

Thomas Jefferson

## Story 12   The Revolutionary War

**PEOPLE**

Patriots

Loyalists

General Thomas Gage

Paul Revere

William Dawes

Captain John Parker

General Cornwallis

**PLACES**

Concord

Lexington

Delaware River

Trenton

Princeton

## Story 13   The Constitution of the United States

**PEOPLE**

Alexander Hamilton

James Madison

# ENRICHMENT IDEAS

**The following higher-level thinking skills questions can be used as discussion starters or as extended learning writing assignments.**

1. Why do you think England, France, and Spain sent people to explore new worlds?

2. Why were teepees a good type of home for the Plains tribes?

3. If you could be part of any First Americans tribe, which tribe would it be and why?

4. How do you think the Pilgrims felt when they first landed at Plymouth Rock?

5. Why were the Quakers the only settlers to live in peace with the native tribes?

6. Would you have been willing to be an indentured servant for the chance to start a new life in America? Explain your answer.

7. Why do you think plantation owners were so cruel to the slaves?

8. Do you think it was unfair for Britain to tax the colonists? Explain your answer.

9. How was the militia different from the British Army?

10. Do you think the Declaration of Independence was a good idea? Explain your answer.

11. How do you think the Patriots were able to win the Revolutionary War?

12. What do you think is the most important part of the Constitution?

13. Why do you think the Constitution has lasted over 200 years?

14. Do you think democracy is a good form of government? Why or Why not?

# ENRICHMENT IDEAS

## Find out more...

- Find out more about what it was like to be an explorer. What were some of the dangers and the conditions on the ships?

- Find out more about the different types of Native American homes: wigwams, teepees, longhouses, chickees. What are the similarities? What are the differences?

- Find out about Acoma Pueblo Village in New Mexico, the oldest continuously inhabited community in North America.

- Find out more about totem poles.

- Find out more about what life was like for a colonist.

- Find out more about what life was like for a slave on a plantation.

- Find out more about the Boston Massacre.

- Find out more about how the Electoral College works.

- Find out more about the Constitution; read the preamble.

- Find out more about checks and balances in government and the separation of powers.

- Find out more about the three branches of government: legislative, executive, and judicial.

## Story 1
**Page 5**
1. They wanted to find new lands and a chance to become rich.
2. Places no European had ever been before.
3. He asked the King and Queen of Spain.
4. He found a new route from Europe to Asia.
5. He found the route from Europe to the Americas.

**Page 7**
1. He was a famous Spanish explorer.
2. He named it Florida.
3. He was looking for a Northwest Passage.
4. They settled around Montreal and the Northeast of America.
5. They wanted to control the fur trade with local natives.

**Page 9**
1. He was an explorer from England.
2. He wanted to sail an English ship to the Pacific Ocean.
3. Queen Elizabeth I asked him.
4. His mission was to attack Spanish ships and steal their treasures.
5. He got a large sum of money and the title of Sir Francis Drake.

**Page 10**
1. discovered 2. route 3. Spanish 4. named 5. looking 6. Fur 7. English 8. mission 9. rewarded

## Story 2
**Page 13**
1. Europeans called them Indians.
2. It had many lakes, rivers, and great forests.
3. They made dishes, pots, tools, canoes, and posts.
4. The most important crop was corn.
5. Corn, beans, and squash were the three sisters.

**Page 15**
1. They came together to live in peace.
2. They lived in upper New York and southeastern Canada.
3. Elder women chose each member.
4. It made important decisions for the tribes.
5. It had a frame of wooden poles covered in elm bark.

**Page 17**
1. They lived in the southern states of America.
2. They planted and harvested crops; gathered nuts, seeds, and fruits; made baskets and pottery.
3. They grew corn, beans, squash, tobacco, and sunflowers.
4. Because of the advanced way they lived and they were wise.
5. It was built off the ground; wood frame, thatch roof; no walls.

**Page 18**
1. Woodland 2. great 3. Planted 4. Live 5. representatives 6. buildings 7. were 8. chickees 9. advanced

## Story 3
**Page 21**
1. About 150,000 people and 60 million buffalo lived on the Plains.
2. They lived in teepees.
3. They traveled on horses.
4. They depended on buffalo.
5. It was used for clothing, blankets, and teepee covers.

**Page 23**
1. They used sign language.
2. They hunted on horseback.
3. They believed in the Great Spirit.
4. The Dakota was the largest and most feared.
5. They treated children with great affection.

**Page 25**
1. They raided their enemies' villages.
2. They took them for protection and strength.
3. It took place in summer.
4. It was done to give thanks to the Great Spirit.
5. It gave people hope for a better future.

**Page 26**
1. buffalo 2. teepees 3. depended 4. sign 5. fierce 6. life 7. there 8. greatest 9. asked

## Story 4
**Page 29**
1. They were made of clay and sandstone.
2. They have lasted over 1,000 years.
3. They were known for their beautiful clay pottery.
4. They raided the villages.
5. Navajo women were well-known for their weaving skills.

**Page 31**
1. They gathered nuts, seeds, roots, and berries.
2. About 50 tribes lived in California.
3. Some were 30 feet long.
4. Acorns was the main part of the Pomo diet.
5. They could be used for cooking and storing food.

**Page 33**
1. It had thick forests, mountains, rivers, lakes, and streams.
2. About 30 tribes lived in the Northwest.
3. They got their food from rivers, the ocean, and the forest.
4. The social classes were nobles, commoners, and slaves.
5. Some totem poles were 50 feet high.

**Page 34**
1. mostly 2. homes 3. known 4. people 5. diet 6. baskets. 7. not 8. almost 9. story

## Story 5
**Page 37**
1. It was named Jamestown.
2. They ran out of food and got sick.
3. The settlers were taking over the land.
4. He came in 1609.
5. They grew tobacco.

**Page 39**
1. Pilgrims were a religious group from England.
2. They landed on Dec. 12, 1620.
3. They lived on the Mayflower.
4. They named it Plymouth.
5. They taught them how to hunt, fish, and grow crops.

**Page 41**
1. They thought the church wasn't pure enough.
2. About 11,000 Puritans set sail.
3. They wanted to set an example of pure and simple living.
4. They were thrown out of the colony.
5. It was dangerous.

Page 42
1. beginning 2. natives 3. tobacco 4. religious 5. winter 6. like
7. pure 8. strict 9. dangerous

## Story 6
Page 45
1. New Hampshire was known as the colony of freedom.
2. They did not want to follow Puritan rules; to start their own settlement.
3. He gave him 12 million acres.
4. He wanted to make money and have a place where Catholics could live in peace.
5. He wanted English farmers.

Page 47
1. They wanted to build their own religious communities.
2. It had very good land for farming.
3. The settlers took over native land; they brought diseases.
4. It was Roger Williams.
5. It became known as a place of religious freedom.

Page 49
1. A group of Englishmen and the governor of Virginia ruled the colony.
2. They came because they were promised land.
3. They had slaves to grow their crops.
4. They were called plantations.
5. They learned from the slaves.

## Story 7
Page 50
1. freedom. 2. gave 3. treated 4. capital 5. diseases 6. escaped
7. from 8. plantation 9. powerful

Page 53
1. It was called New Netherland.
2. They made slavery legal.
3. They started trading with the Iroquois.
4. They would not help them fight their enemies.
5. English and French settlers lived there.

Page 55
1. He was a wealthy Quaker.
2. The king was paying back money he owed Penn's father.
3. He believed in honesty, kindness, and fairness.
4. It made people of all religions equal.
5. They wanted an army.

Page 57
1. They wanted a colony where they could send poor people.
2. They got money.
3. They wanted the colonists to guard the border with Florida.
4. Many slaves worked for rich plantation owners.
5. The thirteen colonies were the beginning.

Page 58
1. named 2. friendly 3. settlers 4. wealthy 5. religions 6. fighting
7. poor 8. slaves 9. thirteen

## Story 8
Page 61
1. They came as indentured servants.
2. They had to work for seven years.
3. They wanted cheap labor.
4. They were cooks, gardeners, housekeepers, field workers, and builders.
5. They were given land and livestock.

Page 63
1. They kidnapped them from their homes. They forced them onto slave ships
2. They wanted to make as much money as possible.
3. It took several months.
4. They were sold at auctions.
5. The families were split up and sold separately.

Page 65
1. They were beaten or killed.
2. They lived in shacks on the plantation.
3. They planted and harvested all the crops; some worked as cooks and maids.
4. They worked from sun up to sundown or longer.
5. There were four million slaves.

Page 66
1. indentured 2. labor 3. property 4. treat 5. enough 6. auctions
7. owned 8. cooks 9. free

## Story 9
Page 69
1. They needed money to pay for wars.
2. It was called the Stamp Act.
3. They became very angry; they would not pay; there were riots in the streets.
4. They sent soldiers.
5. The Boston Massacre happened.

Page 71
1. They were supposed to get tea from the British East India Company.
2. It hurt the tea business.
3. Some protesters dressed up like Native Americans.
4. They dumped 342 chests of tea.
5. It happened o December 16, 1773.

Page 73
1. He ordered them to pay for the tea.
2. They called the laws the Intolerable Acts.
3. British soldiers closed the port of Boston.
4. Over half the men in the city lost their jobs.
5. People from the other colonies sided with Massachusetts.

Page 74
1. war 2. stamp 3. fired 4. popular 5. protesters 6. about
7. ordered 8. close 9. mistake

## Story 10
Page 77
1. They had come to the colonies to be free.
2. The king was determined to control the colonies. The colonists were determined to resist.
3. It had a well-trained army and the largest navy in the world.
4. The British were a mighty force; they had no army.
5. They united to work together against the British.

Page 79
1. Men of all ages, farmers, trappers, doctors, lawyers, and business men all volunteered.
2. They came together to fight for what they believed in.
3. They were specially trained men of the militia; they were the youngest and strongest.
4. They met on September 5, 1774 in Philadelphia.
5. They finally agreed to send a letter to King George.

**Page 81**
1. It took place on May 10, 1775.
2. They were delegates from Massachusetts.
3. They still felt like they were British; they weren't ready to turn away from the king.
4. They all agreed they wanted to win the war.
5. George Washington was the Commander-in-Chief.

**Page 82**
1. free 2. largest 3. defend 4. militia 5. lasted 6. ignored
7. between 8. king 9. delegates

## Story 11
**Page 85**
1. They sent a second letter on July 8, 1775.
2. They asked the king to treat the colonies more fairly.
3. The king refused to read the letter.
4. The future of all the colonists depended on their decision.
5. They decided to declare their independence from Britain.

**Page 87**
1. Thomas Jefferson was chosen to write the document.
2. John Adams and Benjamin Franklin made a few changes.
3. It said all men were created equal and that everyone should have basic rights.
4. It told why the colonists wanted their freedom.
5. It said the colonies were now free and independent states.

**Page 89**
1. It was more common for royalty and the wealthy and powerful to rule the people.
2. They wanted independence from Britain.
3. If signers were caught they could be hanged as traitors.
4. People cheered when they saw the copies. There were parties, bands played, and bells rang.
5. There were fireworks and a big parade.

**Page 90**
1. loyal 2. solve 3. five 4. write 5. days 6. equal 7. voted
8. document 9. win

## Story 12
**Page 93**
1. They wanted to be ready if the British attacked.
2. Paul Revere and William Dawes warned the leaders.
3. It was fired on April 19, 1775.
4. No one knows who fired the first shot.
5. It started the Revolutionary War.

**Page 95**
1. They were still loyal to the King of England.
2. They gathered in New York City.
3. They felt is was useless to fight; they would never be able to win the war.
4. George Washington crossed the Delaware.
5. They felt hopeful and were determined to beat the British.

**Page 97**
1. The French wanted to get back at the British.
2. Spanish soldiers attacked British troops in the south.
3. The last major battle was the Battle of Yorktown.
4. General Cornwallis surrendered his troops.
5. The Treaty of Paris was signed at the end of the war.

**Page 98**
1. secretly 2. soldiers 3. stopped 4. against 5. useless
6. important 7. alongside 8. helped 9. ended

## Story 13
**Page 101**
1. The Constitution was signed in 1787.
2. It creates the federal government.
3. It guarantees certain basic rights for all U.S. citizens.
4. The three branches are the legislative, executive, and judicial.
5. They must work together to run the country.

**Page 103**
1. They decided they needed to set up a federal government.
2. They worked on a document to unite the states.
3. It was completed in 1781.
4. The national government was weak.
5. It could grow and remain safe.

**Page 105**
1. It began on May 25,1787.
2. Rhode Island did not send a delegate.
3. They came together to form a new kind of government.
4. George Washington became the president of the convention.
5. The "Father of the Constitution" was James Madison.

**Page 106**
1. important 2. was 3. federal 4. divided 5. executive 6. sent
7. should 8. citizens 9. written

## Story 14
**Page 109**
1. They were setting up a democracy.
2. One of the most important decisions was about voting.
3. He would be voted into office by the people.
4. They thought it would not be fair; that people would only vote for candidates from their state; that the larger states would have more power.
5. They decided the Electoral College would be the fairest way to vote.

**Page 111**
1. It was in 1789.
2. They believed only people who paid taxes should have a say in the government. They thought only white men were smart enough to vote.
3. Less that 2% could vote.
4. George Washington was elected the first president.
5. John Adams was elected vice president.

**Page 113**
1. Thomas Jefferson, Alexander Hamilton, and Henry Knox were part of the first cabinet.
2. There were 26 senators and 56 representatives.
3. They vote on laws.
4. The make sure federal laws are followed.
5. There were six judges.

**Page 114**
1. democracy 2. office 3. behalf 4. trusted 5. separately 6. leader
7. includes 8. senators 9. six